3 PARTS WELLNESS

3 PARTS WELLNESS

Physical Spiritual Financial

TERIANN D

3 Parts Wellness

CONTENTS

Dedication   vii

PART 1
PHYSICAL   1

   1   Embracing Holistic Wellness   2

   2   The Foundation of Physical Wellness   4

   3   Exercise and Movement   6

   4   Mind Body Connection   8

PART 2
SPIRITUAL   11

   5   Exploring Spirituality   12

   6   Finding Meaning and Purpose   14

   7   Connection and Community   16

PART 3
FINANCIAL   19

   8   Financial Literacy   20

   9   Creating Financial Freedom   22

  10   Aligning Finances with Values   24

  11   Achieving Holistic Harmony   26

12   Embracing Holistic Wellness   28

This book and my life are dedicated first to my four children- Treyvon, Taleena, Calvin and Cameron. And to Jackson, my gift baby. Also to my bonus daughters, Katelynn and Katora. And my bonus son Phillip. They are the reason I feel motivated to keep learning, growing and improving. I love you all so much. Thank you all.

To my husband, Calvin, who is no longer in this realm. I wish he was here. He would have been my number one fan. I can hear him saying, "You did good, baby!" Thank you.

To Chris Hinkley, Calvin's best man in our wedding. He has been there for me so many times since Calvin passed. He took his role as best man to heart and said he felt it was his job, as Calvin's best man, to look out for his family now that he's left. Amazing. Thank you.

There are too many to list all that have positively impacted my life -my mom, my auntie Pam, my cousin Merritt and my best childhood friends Shannon, Mariana, Christy and John all helped to lay the foundation for who I was, who I am and who I am becoming. Thank you all.

Shannon, I love you. You have been so much more than a friend and you helped me get to this point. I love you. Thank you.

I also want to thank Domonique Barbee for starting me on my journey and Dhuwanna Whittington Smith, Tonya Wiley and Kasey Pacheco for helping me find my way by patiently guiding me to valuable resources. I am grateful to be surrounded by so much love, strength and support. These women are truly spectacular. Thank you all.

As I'm writing this, person after person is flooding through my mind. It would surely take another book to list them all. Cherish the ones who pour into your life. To any I've missed, charge it to my mind and space, not my heart.

PART 1

Physical

CHAPTER 1

Embracing Holistic Wellness

As the sun rose over the tranquil horizon, illuminating the world with its gentle rays, Mia found herself contemplating the meaning of true well-being. She had always strived to lead a healthy lifestyle, but lately, she couldn't shake the feeling that something was missing. Little did she know, her journey toward holistic wellness was about to begin.

Holistic wellness, she discovered, was more than just a buzzword; it was a way of life that encompassed every facet of her being. At its core were three key components: physical, spiritual, and financial well-being. Each aspect played a vital role in achieving overall harmony and fulfillment.

The physical component was the foundation upon which all else rested. Mia realized that nurturing her body through regular exercise, nutritious meals, and ample rest was essential for vitality and longevity. She made a commitment to prioritize her physical health, knowing that a strong body was the first step toward holistic wellness.

But physical well-being was only one piece of the puzzle. Mia also recognized the importance of nurturing her spiritual self. Whether through meditation, prayer, or simply connecting with nature, she understood that cultivating inner peace and mindfulness was essential for mental and emotional balance.

As she delved deeper into the concept of holistic wellness, Mia couldn't ignore the significance of financial stability. While money couldn't buy happiness, it did provide security and freedom. She realized that managing her finances wisely, setting goals, and living within her means were crucial steps toward achieving financial well-being.

With newfound clarity, Mia embarked on Part I of her holistic wellness journey: Nurturing the Physical Self. She committed to regular exercise, incorporating a balanced diet into her routine, and prioritizing rest and relaxation. As she took each step forward, she felt a sense of empowerment knowing that she was laying the groundwork for a healthier, happier life.

Little did Mia know, the path to holistic wellness would lead her on a transformative journey of self-discovery, growth, and fulfillment. But for now, she embraced the present moment, ready to embark on the adventure that lay ahead.

CHAPTER 2

The Foundation of Physical Wellness

As Mia delved deeper into her journey toward holistic wellness, she realized that nurturing her physical health was paramount to living a fulfilling life. Physical wellness formed the cornerstone of her well-being, influencing every aspect of her daily existence.

The significance of physical health became abundantly clear to Mia as she reflected on its impact on her daily life. From the moment she woke up in the morning to the time she lay her head down at night, the state of her physical well-being influenced her energy levels, mood, and overall outlook on life.

Maintaining a balanced diet was key to supporting her body's needs and fueling her with the nutrients necessary for optimal functioning. Mia made a conscious effort to fill her plate with a variety of fruits, vegetables, lean proteins, and whole grains, while limiting processed foods and sugary snacks. She found that by listening to her body's hunger and fullness cues, she could better nourish herself and maintain a healthy weight.

In addition to a nutritious diet, Mia recognized the importance of regular exercise in promoting physical wellness. She explored various forms of physical activity, from brisk walks in the park to yoga classes and strength training sessions. Finding activities that she enjoyed made it easier for Mia to stay motivated and consistent with her exercise routine, allowing her to reap the benefits of improved cardiovascular health, strength, and flexibility.

Equally crucial to Mia's physical well-being was prioritizing adequate sleep. She learned that quality sleep was essential for the body to repair and regenerate, as well as for cognitive function and mood regulation. Mia established a relaxing bedtime routine, minimizing screen time before bed and creating a comfortable sleep environment to promote restful slumber.

As Mia embraced the foundation of physical wellness, she discovered that small, sustainable changes to her lifestyle could have a profound impact on her overall health and happiness. By nourishing her body with wholesome foods, staying active, and prioritizing rest, she felt stronger, more energized, and better equipped to tackle life's challenges with resilience and vitality.

CHAPTER 3

Exercise and Movement

In Mia's quest for holistic wellness, she recognized the pivotal role that exercise and movement played in nurturing her physical health. As she delved into the world of fitness, she discovered a myriad of ways to incorporate movement into her daily life, regardless of her fitness level.

Exercise came in many forms, each offering unique benefits for the body and mind. From high-intensity interval training to gentle yoga flows, Mia explored a variety of workouts to find what resonated best with her. She learned that cardiovascular activities like running, cycling, or swimming were excellent for improving heart health and boosting endurance, while strength training exercises such as weightlifting or bodyweight exercises helped build lean muscle mass and increase metabolism.

But exercise wasn't just about sculpting the perfect physique; it was also a powerful tool for managing stress and improving mental well-being. Mia discovered that activities like yoga, Pilates, and tai chi not only strengthened her body but also calmed her mind, reducing anxiety and promoting a sense of inner peace. Even something as simple as a leisurely walk in nature had the power to uplift her spirits and clear her head.

One of the most valuable lessons Mia learned on her journey was that movement didn't have to be confined to the gym or structured workout sessions. She found creative ways to incorporate physical activity into her everyday life, whether it was taking the stairs instead of the elevator, walking or biking instead of driving short distances, or dancing around the house while doing chores.

Regardless of her fitness level, Mia discovered that consistency was key to reaping the benefits of exercise and movement. She made a commitment to prioritize physical activity each day, even if it was just for a few minutes at a time. By listening to her body and honoring its need for movement, she found joy and fulfillment in staying active and embracing a lifestyle of holistic wellness.

CHAPTER 4

Mind Body Connection

As Mia continued her journey toward holistic wellness, she began to delve into the intricate relationship between the mind and body. In Chapter 4, she explored the profound impact of the mind-body connection on her overall health and well-being.

Mia discovered that mental and physical health were deeply intertwined, with each influencing the other in profound ways. When she felt stressed or anxious, she noticed physical symptoms like tension in her muscles or an upset stomach. Conversely, when she prioritized self-care and practiced mindfulness, she experienced a greater sense of ease and vitality in both mind and body.

Managing stress became a priority for Mia as she navigated the demands of daily life. She explored various techniques to cultivate relaxation and inner peace, such as deep breathing exercises, meditation, and progressive muscle relaxation. These practices not only helped her to alleviate stress in the moment but also fostered a sense of resilience and emotional balance over time.

Improving mental clarity was another area of focus for Mia on her journey toward holistic wellness. She recognized the importance of decluttering her mind and creating space for clarity and creativity to flourish. Journaling, mindfulness meditation, and engaging in activities that brought her joy and fulfillment were powerful tools for sharpening her focus and enhancing mental clarity.

Mia also discovered the profound impact of positive thinking on her overall well-being. By cultivating a mindset of gratitude, optimism, and self-compassion, she nurtured her mental and emotional health, paving the way for greater resilience and happiness.

As she continued to explore the mind-body connection, Mia felt a deep sense of awe and reverence for the interconnectedness of all aspects of her being. She realized that true wellness encompassed not only physical health but also mental, emotional, and spiritual vitality. With each step on her journey, she grew more attuned to the wisdom of her body and the power of her mind, laying the foundation for a life of holistic wellness.

With a newfound understanding of the mind-body connection, Mia eagerly anticipated Part II of her journey: Cultivating Spiritual Growth. She embraced the opportunity to deepen her connection to herself and the world around her, knowing that true fulfillment awaited on the path ahead.

PART 2

Spiritual

CHAPTER 5

Exploring Spirituality

As Mia embarked on the second part of her journey toward holistic wellness, she felt a sense of anticipation and curiosity swirling within her. Part II, dedicated to Cultivating Spiritual Growth, promised to delve into the depths of her soul and explore the profound mysteries of existence.

This marked the beginning of Mia's exploration into spirituality—a journey of self-discovery, connection, and transcendence. For Mia, spirituality encompassed a deep sense of inner knowing, a connection to something greater than herself, and a reverence for the sacredness of life.

As she delved into the vast and multifaceted realm of spirituality, Mia encountered a myriad of beliefs, practices, and traditions from around the world. From ancient wisdom teachings to modern spiritual practices, she discovered a rich tapestry of spiritual paths, each offering its own unique insights and truths.

Mia approached her exploration of spirituality with an open heart and mind, allowing herself to be guided by intuition and inner wisdom. She sought out experiences that nourished her soul and resonated with her deepest truths, whether it was through meditation, prayer, ritual, or communion with nature.

One of the key aspects of Mia's spiritual journey was the cultivation of presence and mindfulness. She learned to quiet the chatter of her mind and immerse herself fully in the present moment, where she discovered a profound sense of peace and connection to the divine.

Mia also explored the concept of interconnectedness—the idea that all living beings are inherently connected and part of a larger, universal whole. This realization filled her with a sense of awe and wonder, deepening her appreciation for the beauty and sacredness of life.

As Mia continued to explore spirituality, she found herself drawn to practices that nourished her soul and aligned with her values and beliefs. Each step on her spiritual journey brought her closer to a deeper understanding of herself and the world around her, paving the way for greater fulfillment, purpose, and joy.

With each passing day, Mia felt her spirit expanding and her heart opening to the infinite possibilities that lay before her. As she embraced the transformative power of spirituality, she knew that she was embarking on a journey of profound growth and awakening—a journey that would lead her ever closer to the essence of her truest self.

CHAPTER 6

Finding Meaning and Purpose

As Mia delved deeper into her spiritual journey, she found herself contemplating the age-old questions of meaning and purpose. In Chapter 6, she embarked on a quest to uncover the unique calling that resided within her soul and to align her life with her deepest values and beliefs.

Finding meaning and purpose, Mia discovered, was not an external pursuit but an inner journey of self-discovery and self-realization. It required delving into the depths of her being, exploring her passions, talents, and desires, and uncovering the essence of who she truly was.

Reflecting on her personal values and beliefs became a cornerstone of Mia's quest for meaning and purpose. She took time to identify the principles that guided her life—the ideals she held dear and the truths she held sacred. By aligning her actions with these spiritual principles, she found greater clarity and direction in her path forward.

Mia also recognized the importance of listening to the whispers of her heart—the subtle nudges and intuitive insights that pointed her toward her true calling. She engaged in practices like journaling, meditation, and quiet contemplation to connect with her inner wisdom and discern the next steps on her journey.

But finding meaning and purpose wasn't just about self-discovery; it was also about service and contribution to others and the world. Mia felt a deep sense of fulfillment when she used her gifts and talents to make a positive impact in the lives of others, whether through acts of kindness, volunteering, or pursuing a career aligned with her passions and values.

Living a fulfilling life, Mia realized, was about more than just achieving external success or material wealth. It was about nurturing her spirit, cultivating meaningful connections, and making a difference in the world. She embraced each day as an opportunity to live in alignment with her soul's purpose, knowing that true fulfillment lay in following the whispers of her heart.

As Mia continued on her journey of self-discovery and spiritual growth, she found solace in the knowledge that her life had meaning and purpose—a purpose that was uniquely hers to fulfill. With each step she took toward alignment with her deepest values and beliefs, she felt a greater sense of fulfillment and joy, knowing that she was living a life of purpose and meaning.

Connection and Community

In the tapestry of Mia's spiritual journey, Chapter 7 illuminated the profound significance of connection and community. As she delved deeper into her quest for holistic wellness, she realized that nurturing relationships and fostering a sense of belonging were essential pillars of her journey.

Connection, Mia discovered, was the thread that wove together the fabric of human experience. It was the invisible bond that linked souls together, transcending boundaries of time, space, and circumstance. Whether through laughter shared with friends, heartfelt conversations with loved ones, or acts of kindness toward strangers, Mia found that connection was the heartbeat of her existence.

Community, she learned, provided the fertile soil in which connection could flourish. It was the tribe of like-minded souls who supported, uplifted, and inspired one another on their respective journeys. Whether bound by shared interests, beliefs, or experiences, community offered a sense of belonging and acceptance that nourished the soul.

Mia recognized the importance of engaging in meaningful connections with others, both within her immediate circle and beyond. She made an effort to cultivate authentic relationships built on trust, empathy, and mutual respect, knowing that these connections enriched her life in countless ways.

But connection wasn't just about the bonds we formed with others; it was also about the relationship we cultivated with ourselves. Mia learned that true connection began from within—that by embracing her authentic self and honoring her innermost truths, she could forge deeper, more meaningful connections with others.

As Mia immersed herself in her community, she discovered a sense of purpose and belonging that filled her with gratitude and joy. Whether volunteering at a local charity, participating in group meditation sessions, or attending spiritual gatherings, she found fulfillment in contributing to a supportive community and uplifting others along the way.

In the interconnected web of life, Mia realized that her journey toward holistic wellness was intertwined with the journeys of those around her. Through connection and community, she found strength, inspiration, and the profound realization that she was never alone— that, in the vast tapestry of existence, she was an integral thread, bound to the hearts of all who shared in the journey of life.

PART 3

Financial

Financial Literacy

As Mia journeyed deeper into her pursuit of holistic wellness, she encountered Chapter 8—a pivotal exploration into the realm of financial literacy. Understanding the importance of financial well-being in achieving overall harmony, Mia embarked on a journey to master basic financial principles and secure her financial future.

Financial literacy, Mia discovered, was the foundation upon which her financial well-being rested. It encompassed a range of essential skills and knowledge, from budgeting and saving to investing and planning for the future. Armed with this understanding, Mia set out to empower herself with the tools and strategies needed to navigate the complex world of personal finance.

Budgeting emerged as the cornerstone of Mia's financial journey. She learned to create a detailed budget that accounted for her income, expenses, and savings goals, allowing her to track her spending and make informed financial decisions. By living within her means and prioritizing her financial goals, Mia gained greater control over her finances and laid the groundwork for financial stability.

Saving became a top priority for Mia as she recognized the importance of building a financial safety net for herself and her future. She established an emergency fund to cover unexpected expenses and set aside funds for long-term goals, such as homeownership, travel, and retirement. Through consistent saving habits and prudent financial management, Mia built a foundation of financial security that provided peace of mind and stability.

But financial literacy went beyond budgeting and saving—it also encompassed strategies for managing debt, building credit, and planning for the future. Mia learned to use credit responsibly, paying off her debts on time and in full to maintain a positive credit history. She explored investment options to grow her wealth over time, seeking guidance from financial professionals to make informed decisions aligned with her goals and risk tolerance.

As Mia delved deeper into the world of financial literacy, she felt empowered to take control of her financial future and create a life of abundance and prosperity. By mastering basic financial principles, she gained the confidence to navigate life's financial challenges and seize opportunities for growth and wealth accumulation.

With each step forward on her journey toward financial literacy, Mia felt a sense of empowerment and liberation, knowing that she held the keys to her financial destiny. Armed with knowledge, skills, and a clear vision for the future, she embraced the path ahead with confidence and determination, knowing that financial well-being was an essential component of her journey toward holistic wellness.

Creating Financial Freedom

In Chapter 9 of Mia's journey toward holistic wellness, she delved into the realm of financial freedom—a state of abundance and empowerment where she had the flexibility and resources to live life on her own terms. With a newfound understanding of financial literacy, Mia embarked on a path to set ambitious goals and develop a plan to achieve them.

Setting financial goals became a cornerstone of Mia's journey toward financial freedom. She took time to reflect on her values, aspirations, and dreams, identifying both short-term and long-term objectives that would bring her closer to her vision of financial independence. Whether it was saving for a dream vacation, purchasing a home, or retiring early, Mia knew that clarity and intentionality were essential to manifesting her financial desires.

With her goals in sight, Mia developed a strategic plan to achieve them. She broke down her goals into actionable steps, creating timelines and milestones to track her progress along the way. Mia knew that consistency and discipline were key to success, so she committed to sticking to her plan and making adjustments as needed to stay on course.

As Mia pursued her financial goals, she explored strategies for generating passive income and diversifying her revenue streams. She invested in income-generating assets such as rental properties, dividend-paying stocks, and peer-to-peer lending platforms, leveraging the power of compounding interest and passive income to build wealth over time. By diversifying her income sources, Mia reduced her reliance on a single source of income and increased her financial resilience in the face of economic uncertainty.

Achieving financial independence became Mia's ultimate goal—a state where she could sustain her desired lifestyle without having to rely on traditional employment or active income streams. She envisioned a life of freedom and abundance, where she had the time and resources to pursue her passions, travel the world, and give back to causes she cared about deeply.

With unwavering determination and a clear vision for the future, Mia continued on her journey toward financial freedom. She knew that the path ahead would be filled with challenges and obstacles, but she embraced each challenge as an opportunity for growth and learning. With each step forward, she drew closer to her goal of financial independence, knowing that the journey itself was as rewarding as the destination.

As Mia neared the culmination of her journey toward financial freedom, she reflected on how far she had come and felt a deep sense of gratitude for the abundance and prosperity that surrounded her. With a solid foundation of financial literacy and a clear plan for the future, she knew that she was well-equipped to achieve her dreams and create a life of true abundance and fulfillment.

Aligning Finances with Values

In Chapter 10 of Mia's journey toward holistic wellness, she delved into the intricate relationship between money and personal values. As she continued to explore the realm of financial freedom, Mia realized the importance of aligning her finances with her deepest beliefs and priorities.

Examining the relationship between money and personal values was a profound journey of self-discovery for Mia. She took time to reflect on what truly mattered to her—the principles and ideals that guided her life and shaped her decisions. Whether it was family, community, environmental sustainability, or social justice, Mia knew that her values were the compass that would guide her financial choices.

Practicing conscious spending became a cornerstone of Mia's approach to aligning her finances with her values. She became mindful of where her money was going, choosing to support companies and businesses that aligned with her beliefs and made a positive impact on the world. Whether it was buying from local, ethically sourced vendors or investing in socially responsible companies, Mia knew that every dollar she spent was a vote for the kind of world she wanted to live in.

But conscious spending wasn't just about where Mia spent her money—it was also about where she chose not to spend it. She became intentional about avoiding purchases that didn't align with her values or bring true fulfillment and joy into her life. By prioritizing experiences over material possessions and practicing gratitude for what she already had, Mia found greater contentment and abundance in her life.

Investing also played a crucial role in aligning Mia's finances with her values. She sought out investment opportunities that aligned with her beliefs, whether it was investing in renewable energy companies, supporting women and minority-owned businesses, or divesting from industries that harmed the environment or exploited workers. By investing her money in ways that aligned with her values, Mia not only grew her wealth but also made a positive impact on the world.

As Mia continued on her journey of aligning her finances with her values, she felt a deep sense of alignment and purpose in her life. She knew that by honoring her values in her financial decisions, she was not only building a secure future for herself but also contributing to a more just, equitable, and sustainable world for future generations. With each dollar she spent and each investment she made, Mia felt empowered to create positive change and live a life of true abundance and fulfillment.

CHAPTER 11

Achieving Holistic Harmony

In the final chapter of Mia's transformative journey toward holistic wellness, she embraced the profound realization that true harmony and fulfillment were found in the integration of mind, body, and spirit. Chapter 11 marked the culmination of her quest—a synthesis of the lessons learned from each aspect of wellness to create a balanced and fulfilling life.

Bringing together the lessons learned from each aspect of wellness, Mia embarked on the journey of achieving holistic harmony—a state of alignment and integration where she thrived in all areas of her life. She understood that true wellness extended beyond physical health to encompass mental, emotional, and spiritual well-being, and she committed to nurturing each aspect with care and intention.

Mia found that maintaining holistic harmony required ongoing dedication and mindfulness. She continued to prioritize her physical health through regular exercise, nourishing foods, and ample rest, knowing that a strong body was the foundation for overall well-being.

At the same time, Mia cultivated her spiritual growth through practices like meditation, mindfulness, and connection with nature. She embraced moments of stillness and reflection, allowing herself to tap into the wisdom of her soul and deepen her connection to something greater than herself.

Embracing connection and community remained a central focus for Mia as she journeyed toward holistic harmony. She cherished her relationships with loved ones and sought out opportunities to give back to her community, knowing that true fulfillment was found in the bonds we shared and the impact we made on the world around us.

But perhaps most importantly, Mia learned to listen to the whispers of her heart and follow the guidance of her inner wisdom. She trusted herself to make decisions aligned with her values and beliefs, knowing that true fulfillment came from living authentically and in alignment with her deepest truths.

As Mia reflected on her journey, she felt a deep sense of gratitude for the lessons learned and the growth experienced along the way. She knew that achieving holistic harmony was not a destination but a lifelong journey—a journey of self-discovery, growth, and transformation.

With each passing day, Mia felt more empowered to live a life of purpose, passion, and joy. She knew that by continuing to prioritize her wellness and nurture all aspects of her being, she would continue to grow and thrive in all areas of her life. With a heart full of gratitude and a spirit of adventure, Mia embraced the path ahead, knowing that the journey toward holistic harmony was the greatest gift of all.

CHAPTER 12

Embracing Holistic Wellness

As Mia's transformative journey toward holistic wellness comes to a close, it's essential to reflect on the key takeaways and encourage readers to embark on their own path toward holistic well-being.

Throughout her journey, Mia discovered that true wellness encompasses every aspect of our being—physical, mental, emotional, and spiritual. It's about nurturing our bodies, minds, and souls in harmony to live a balanced and fulfilling life.

The journey toward holistic wellness is not a destination but an ongoing process of self-discovery, growth, and transformation. It requires commitment, dedication, and a willingness to prioritize self-care in all its forms.

Key takeaways from Mia's journey include:

Nurturing the Physical Self: Prioritize your physical health through regular exercise, balanced nutrition, and adequate rest. Your body is the vessel through which you experience life, so treat it with care and respect.

Cultivating Spiritual Growth: Explore practices that nourish your soul and deepen your connection to yourself and the world around you. Whether through meditation, prayer, or spending time in nature, cultivate a sense of inner peace and purpose.

Managing Finances Wisely: Take control of your financial well-being by understanding basic financial principles, setting goals, and developing a plan to achieve them. Align your financial decisions with your values and beliefs to create a life of abundance and prosperity.

Fostering Connection and Community: Prioritize meaningful relationships and cultivate a sense of belonging within your community. Connection with others enriches our lives and provides support and encouragement along the journey.

Aligning Finances with Values: Practice conscious spending and investing in ways that align with your beliefs and priorities. By honoring your values in your financial decisions, you create a life of purpose and meaning.

It's important to remember that the journey toward holistic wellness is unique to each individual. There is no one-size-fits-all approach, and it's okay to explore different paths and find what works best for you.

Above all, remember that self-care is not selfish—it's essential. Prioritize your well-being in all its forms, and remember that your journey toward holistic wellness is a lifelong adventure filled with opportunities for growth, healing, and joy.

So, to all those embarking on their journey toward holistic wellness, may you embrace the path with an open heart and mind, knowing that true well-being awaits those who dare to seek it.